£6.99

CONTENTS

This book belongs to:

JUNGLE FEVER!

Can you spot the 12 animals in the grid below?

D	R	A	P	O	E	L	G	W	S
A	C	R	O	C	O	D	I	L	E
Y	E	K	N	O	M	S	R	K	L
G	F	O	W	B	N	W	A	D	E
O	P	I	N	A	R	E	F	G	P
R	S	T	K	T	H	A	F	W	H
I	W	E	X	N	I	K	E	L	A
L	K	D	O	W	N	G	W	D	N
L	H	I	P	P	O	H	E	W	T
A	L	W	B	O	Z	E	B	R	A

Answers on page 61 ⇨

5

THE GREAT TAZ HUNT *

Writer: Dave King   Artist: George Wildman   Letterer: Nick Napolitano

PART 1

MONDAY MORNING, A STRANGE AND HORRIBLE WAILING ECHOES FROM THE CITY ZOO...

AAAARRGH!!

AAWOOOOOOO!

AND WHAT IS THIS FEARFUL NOISE? IS IT THE CRY OF SOME POOR BEAST BELLOWING IN TERROR?

WELL...

AOOWWWW!

THIS IS TERRIBLE!

UNDERHILL, GET A HOLD OF YOURSELF, THIS IS NO TIME FOR HYSTERICS!

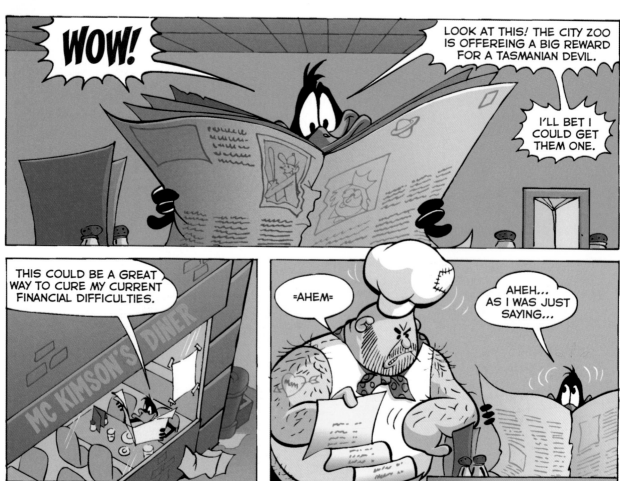

WOW!

LOOK AT THIS! THE CITY ZOO IS OFFEREING A BIG REWARD FOR A TASMANIAN DEVIL.

I'LL BET I COULD GET THEM ONE.

THIS COULD BE A GREAT WAY TO CURE MY CURRENT FINANCIAL DIFFICULTIES.

MC KIMSON'S DINER

=AHEM=

AHEH... AS I WAS JUST SAYING...

SEVERAL HOURS LATER...

OF COURSE, FINDING A TASMANIAN DEVIL DEPENDS ON BEING ABLE TO LEAVE THIS KITCHEN IN THE NEXT FIFTY YEARS OR SO!

SEVERAL HOURS LATER...

AN' DON'T COME BACK YA' LOUSY FREELOADER!

STAFF ONLY

CRASH

TWEET

HMMM... I MUST RECOMMEND THIS PLACE TO ALL MY FRIENDS! =SIGH=

JUICE

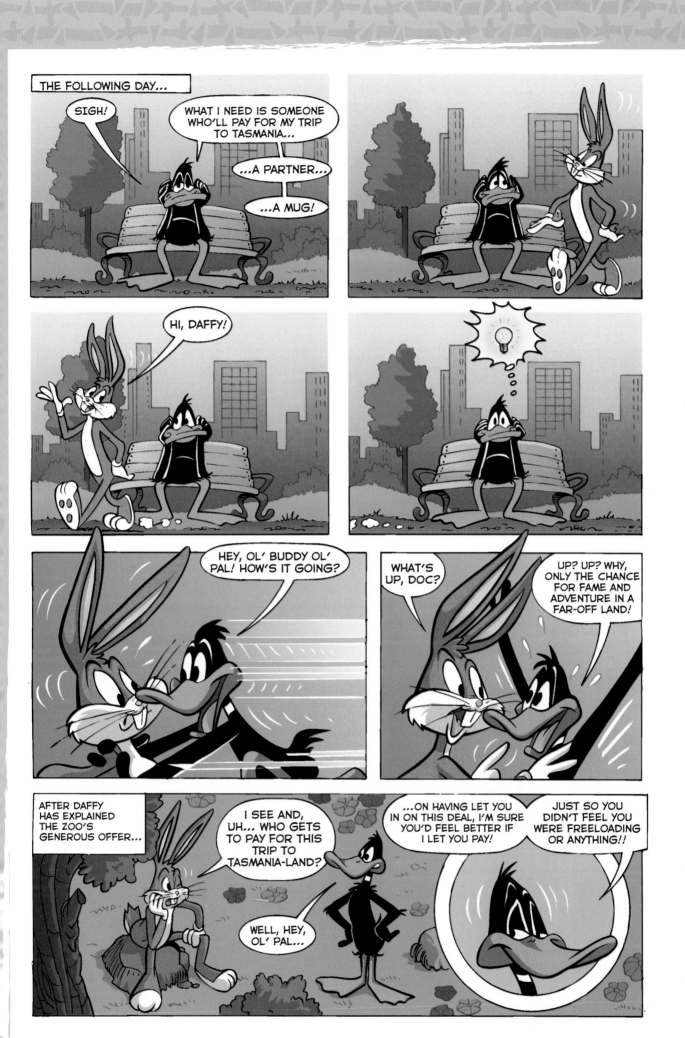

Continued on page 18 →

Daft Drawings!

Copy the picture of Taz square by square, then colour him in.

SUPER SAFARI

BINOCULARS

You will need:

Cardboard tube, PVA glue, torn-up newspaper, paints and paintbrush, sticky tape, card, black cord or ribbon

1 Cut the cardboard tube in half. Next cut two identical pieces of card and two pieces slightly larger. Wrap each one into a tube shape, you now have a total of six tubes.

2 Stack the tubes into two piles, in size order. Tape them together, to make the two separate sections of the binoculars.

3 Wrap thin strips of card around the top and base of each section. Then cover each piece with a layer of torn-up newspaper and glue. Wrap a band of card around the tubes to join them together. Add more newspaper and glue, leave to dry. Paint the binoculars black. When dry, glue the ends of a length of cord to the binoculars.

SET!

To make your own safari hat and binoculars, follow the steps below.

SAFARI HAT

You will need: PVA glue, torn-up newspaper, paints and paintbrush, sticky tape, card, large balloon

1 Blow up the balloon. Cover the top half with 4-5 layers of torn-up newspaper and PVA glue. Leave to dry then pop the balloon.

2 Trim the edge of the balloon. Draw around it onto card. Draw another circle around the outside of the first. Cut out the ring that you have made, then make four snips.

3 Use sticky tape to fix the four pieces of card around the base of the hat. Add a small circle of card to the top. Cover the whole thing with two layers of torn-up newspaper and glue. When it's dry, paint the hat light green.

Continued from page 14

Spot The Difference

See if you can spot the 10 differences between the two pictures below.

Answers on page 61 ⇒

27

Answers on page 61 ⇒

Treasure Trail!

INVITE SOME FRIENDS OVER AND HAVE YOUR VERY OWN TREASURE HUNT. FOLLOW THE INSTRUCTIONS BELOW TO FIND OUT HOW.

Using the template map over the page, draw an overhead view of your house and garden. Don't forget details like the garage, shed, trees, pond and flowerbeds!

Ask your parents to hide some treasure in a secret spot for you and your friends to find. They will also need to leave clues hidden around the garden. Using your map, hunt out the treasure!

Make sure you have your safari hat and binoculars from pages 16 and 17!

Give us a clue!?

Your parents could use some of the clues below:

Starting at the front door, walk 10 paces forward, then turn to your right, look all around for clue number two.

Turn around 3 times then walk sideways 5 paces. You will find your next clue near a potted plant.

For clue number 3, think where gardening tools are stored. This is where your next clue is hidden.

Why not set up camp in your garden? Use an old sheet and a few chairs for a perfect place to rest your weary legs!

They could also leave riddles for you to solve like this:

I am tall and green with long, heavy arms. I grow small egg-shaped things that squirrels like to eat. Come and find me for your next clue!

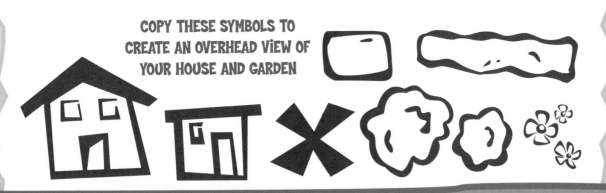

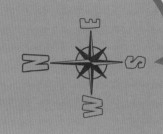

TREASURE MAP

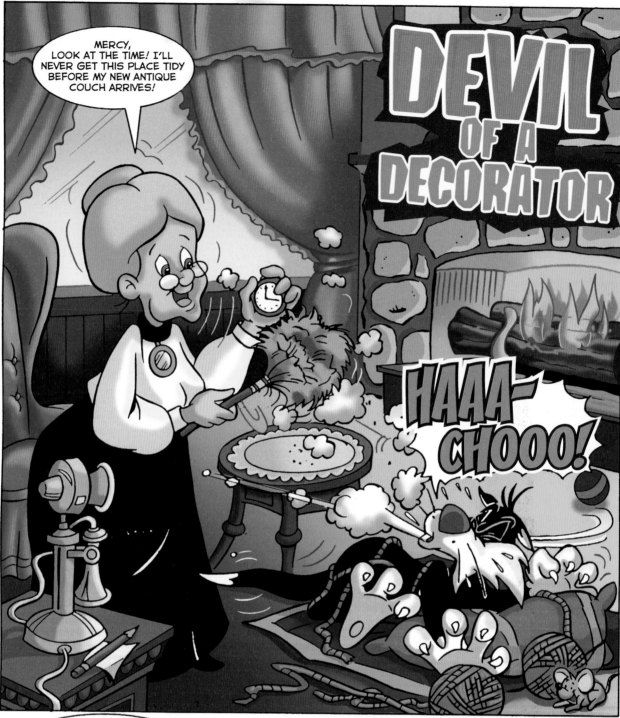

DEVIL OF A DECORATOR

FIRST THING WE NEED IS SOMETHING FOR YOUR THROAT!

IT'S MY OWN FORMULA -- COUGH SYRUP, CASTER OIL AND RED CHILLI SAUCE!

MY, YOU FEEL FEVERISH! WE'LL HAVE TO BRING THAT TEMPERATURE DOWN!

AHHHH...

SSSSSSS

CHK CHK CHK CHK CHK

OVERDID IT A MITE DID WE? DOCTOR GRANNY HAS THE SOLUTION!

BRZZZZ

SLAM

YI YI YI YI YI!

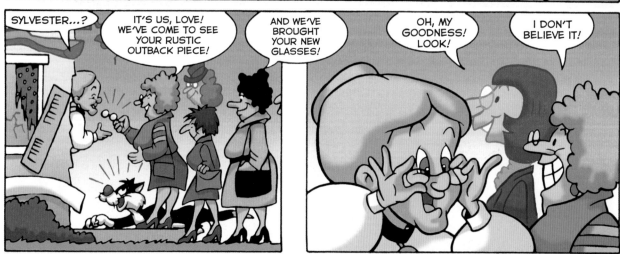

SYLVESTER...?

IT'S US, LOVE! WE'VE COME TO SEE YOUR RUSTIC OUTBACK PIECE!

AND WE'VE BROUGHT YOUR NEW GLASSES!

OH, MY GOODNESS! LOOK!

I DON'T BELIEVE IT!

ANIMAL CRACKERS!

Test your knowledge of the great animal kingdom with this wacky wildlife quiz! For help try looking in books or on the internet.

1 What is the fastest land animal?

DID YOU KNOW...? A hippo can run faster than a man.

2 Which animal is the biggest wild cat?

DID YOU KNOW...? A lion's roar can be heard from five miles away.

3 How many species of elephant are there?

4 What is a group of lions called?

5 What is the largest land animal?

DID YOU KNOW...? Giraffes have no vocal chords

6 What is a striped horse-like animal called?

7 Which reptile can live on land and in water?

DID YOU KNOW...? Elephants are the only mammals that can't jump.

8 What kind of animal is a Red Howler?

DID YOU KNOW...? African elephants only have four teeth to chew their food with.

9 How many types of rhino are there?

DID YOU KNOW...? Camels chew in a figure of 8 pattern.

10 Which land mammal has the largest eyes?

Answers on page 61

TAZ HUNGRY #@*$%!!!

ACME ANIMALS RESEARCH

WB1437

VERN! VERN! HE'S LOOSE!

YOU WANT ME TO CATCH HIM YOU'RE CRAZY

GIMME YOUR LUNCH, MILO - OR ELSE!

YOU WISH, BUTCH! GO PICK ON SOMEONE YOUR OWN SIZE!

OH, RIGHT... THERE IS NO ONE YOUR OWN SIZE!

HAND IT OVER, SHRIMP!

SHRIMP? SHRIMP?? YOU OBVIOUSLY HAVEN'T NOTICED MY RAZOR-SHARP TEETH, AND MY UH, HUGE MUSCLED ARMS, AND MY... BREATH OF DEATH! I'M LETHAL! I'M WARNING YOU!

J-JUST DON'T HURT ME! PLEASE!!

WELL, I SURE SHOWED HIM! HE WON'T MESS WITH ME AGAIN!

BIG TAZ ON CAMPUS

43

COLOUR CRAZY!

Add a splash of colour to Taz and Bugs!

51

SAY WHAT?!

Write your own captions in the speech bubbles to finish off these crazy scenes!

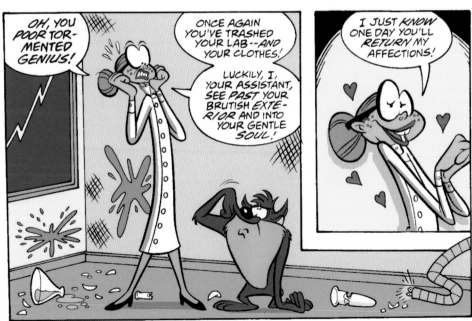

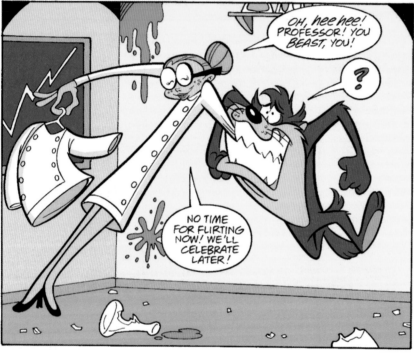

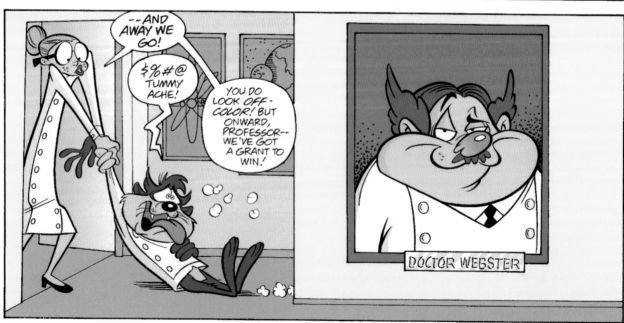

DOCTOR WEBSTER

ANSWERS

P5 Jungle Fever

D	R	A	P	O	E	L	G	W	S
A	C	R	O	C	O	D	I	L	E
Y	E	K	N	O	M	S	R	K	L
G	F	O	W	B	N	W	A	D	E
O	P	I	N	A	R	E	F	G	P
R	S	T	K	T	H	A	F	W	H
I	W	E	X	N	I	K	E	L	A
L	K	D	O	W	N	G	W	D	N
L	H	I	P	P	O	H	E	W	T
A	L	W	B	O	Z	E	B	R	A

P27 Spot the Difference

P28-29 Undercover

P42 Animal Crackers

1. A cheetah runs at 70mph
2. A tiger
3. 2, Asian and African
4. A pride
5. An elephant
6. A zebra
7. A crocodile
8. A monkey
9. 5, White, Black, Indian, Javan and Sumatran
10. The giraffe